HERE'S **HEATHCLIFF** by Geo Gately

AMERICA'S CRAZIEST CAT!

Volume V

© McNaught Synd., Inc.

THE BEST OF SUNDAY WITH HEATHCLIFF

HEATHCLIFF

THE BEST OF FRIENDS

TOR

A TOM DOHERTY ASSOCIATES BOOK

A TOR Book
Published by Tom Doherty Associates, Inc.
49 West 24 Street
New York, NY 10010

ISBN: 0-812-50017-2   Can. ISBN: 0-812-50018-0

Printed in the United States of America

0 9 8 7 6 5 4 3 2

MOOSE-CALL HORN

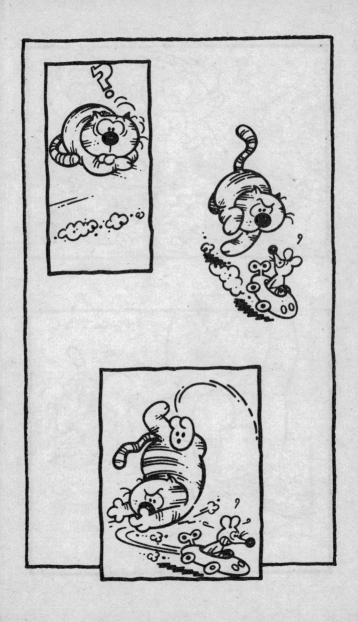

PUZZLE

2-12 © 1978
McNaught Synd., Inc.

THE CHALLENGE

by Geo Gately

WE DON'T NEED A SIGN FOR THAT BIG SISSY!

ARE YOU KIDDING?! HE'S A GREAT WATCHDOG!!

ANSWERING SERVICE

HERE COMES THE TELEVISION REPAIRMAN WITH OUR NEW PICTURE TUBE!

FASTER THAN A SPEEDING WOMBAT...

by Geo Gately

SUPER HERO

BIRDIE WITH A GIFT OF GAB

by Geg Gately

WELL, LOOK HERE!... THE NUTMEGS HAVE INSTALLED A BIRDY BATHING FACILITY!

AT LEAST IT'S GOOD FOR SOMETHING!

by Geg Gately

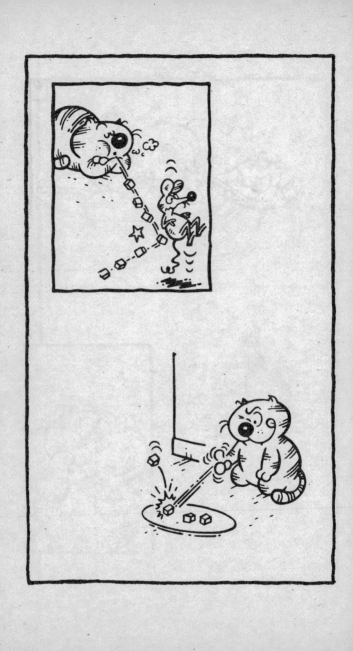

WELL!—LOOK WHO'S IN THE LEMONADE BUSINESS!

CLUG! CLUG! CLUG!

C'MON, HEATHCLIFF!... WE'RE GOING
BEACHCOMBING... WE'LL LOOK FOR
SHELLS AND STUFF!

HEATHCLIFF
TO THE RESCUE!

by Geo Gately

FIRST OF THE MONTH AGAIN

by Geg Cately

HEATHCLIFF

AMERICA'S CRAZIEST CAT